The Curious World
of the Crab

Books by Joseph J. Cook and William L. Wisner

The Nightmare World of the Shark
The Phantom World of the Octopus and Squid
Warrior Whale
Killer Whale!

By Joseph J. Cook

The Curious World of the Crab

By Joseph J. Cook and William J. Romeika

Better Surfing for Boys

WORLD OF THE CRAB

By Joseph J. Cook

Illustrated with photographs and diagrams

DODD, MEAD & COMPANY · NEW YORK

To Peggy and Mary Jane Ferguson

ACKNOWLEDGMENT

The author particularly wishes to thank the following: Alaska Department of Fish and Game; The American Museum of Natural History, New York City; The British Museum of Natural History, London; The Chesapeake Biological Laboratory of the Maryland Department of Research and Education; Florida Board of Conservation; Marineland of Florida; Marine Resources Operations Laboratory of the California Department of Fish and Game; the Texas Parks and Wildlife Department; and Dr. Waldo L. Schmitt, author of *Crustaceans*, published by the University of Michigan Press.

Library of Congress Catalog Card Number: 71-105288

Printed in the United States of America

Contents

1. Crustaceans

Swimming, running, and crawling through the oceans, bays, and some fresh-water bodies of the earth, there is a group of shell-covered creatures known as crustaceans. Chiefly marine animals, some crustaceans do occur in fresh water, while still others prefer to live in damp earth or sand.

There are about twenty thousand recognized species of crustaceans, ranging from microscopic size to giants with lengths of ten feet or more. The most commonly known to man are crabs, lobsters, shrimp, crayfish, and barnacles.

Crustaceans are invertebrates, that is, without backbones, and they are arthropods or joint-footed animals. They have a protective external skeleton, or hard shell, covering their bodies, and are commonly called shellfish. The name *Crustacea*, which is derived from the Latin word *crusta*, means crust or shell. This shell contains chitin (kí-tin), a horny, flexible substance somewhat like a fingernail. In crustaceans it may be as hard as bone, or tough and leathery, or sometimes thin and transparent. The hardness of the body-covering depends on the amount of lime present.

The calico crab, like other crustaceans, wears its skeleton on the outside of its body, and is a joint-footed animal.

Marineland of Florida

Crustaceans, therefore, are animals that wear their skeletons on the outside of their bodies. The covering of a crustacean is similar to a suit of armor and helps protect the animal from its enemies.

The body within the shell is composed of many segments which are usually combined or fused to form two main body sections: the cephalothorax, made up of head and thorax, and the abdomen. Each body segment has paired appendages which differ in number and usage according to the species.

Crustaceans are also characterized by two pairs of antennae, the use of gills for breathing, and eyes which in many species are mounted on movable stalks.

Like mollusks, crustaceans have blood that is pale blue. The color is caused by a copper mineral in the water that the animal absorbs. Man and many other kinds of animals have iron rather than copper in their blood, the iron making the blood red.

Mammals are known as warm-blooded animals in that they have a certain body temperature no matter what the outside temperature is. Crustaceans are not mammals and they are not warm-blooded. The crustacean's body heat is neither more nor less than that of the water or the air around it. When the weather is hot, all the chemical reactions and activities of its body are fast; when it is cold, its reactions are slow and sluggish. In winter or extreme cold weather it is sometimes difficult to tell if a crustacean is alive or dead.

Crustaceans made their first appearance on the earth approximately 500 to 600 million years ago. They are the relatives of some of the oldest living creatures in the world. One animal commonly but wrongly called a crustacean is the horseshoe crab,

New York State Museum

These fossil tracks, found in rocks in eastern North America, are between 5 and 6½ inches wide and were made half a billion years ago. Donald W. Fisher, New York's State Paleontologist, thinks that the fossil trails may have been made by creatures that were related to the horseshoe crab, which leaves a similar trail.

known as a "living fossil." This "living fossil" comes from a family that goes back for hundreds of millions of years. Its ancestors inhabited the seas of the world long before the dinosaurs made their appearance on the earth.

Today, the crustacean family is widely varied since these animals have adapted to many different ways of life. The majority are free-living, but some are sedentary, or remain in one locality. Some species are solitary, while others live in large groups or colonies.

Because of their abundance in the ocean, crustaceans are sometimes called "the insects of the sea." Most of them are an important source of food for fish and some are of considerable value throughout the world as food for man.

The blue crab (true or brachyuran) is an excellent swimmer. Notice the last legs are shaped like paddles. These help propel him through the water.

Texas Parks and Wildlife Department

2. The Crab

Crabs belong to the order Decapoda, and are divided into two sections. True or brachyuran crabs have five pairs of legs visible, as in the blue crab. In the anomuran type, such as the king crab, the last pair of walking legs is very small and folded within the gill chamber. There are over five thousand known species between these two sections of crabs.

The crab can be numbered among the many creatures that are not quite sure whether they prefer to live in the sea or on the land. Some crabs leave the sea and return only at certain seasons of the year. Others live in burrows in the banks of salty tidal streams. Some, like the Lenten crab of southern Europe, live in fresh water rivers, ponds, and lakes. Other crabs live in the sheltering shells of mussels and oysters, where they share the food of their hosts. This is known as commensal living, which literally means "being at the table together."

The name crab is applied to the short-tailed decapod or ten-legged crustacean. Crabs are easily distinguished from such crustaceans as the long-tailed shrimp and

the lobster, first, by their general appearance, and then by their small abdomen or "tail" which is kept folded under the body where it fits into a groove. The narrow T-shape of the male's abdomen distinguishes it from the broad and rounded abdomen of the female crab.

Most crabs have a more or less flattened, oval shape, and are quite broad from side to side. A hard shell completely encloses the soft body or cephalothorax of the crab. The top of the shell is called the carapace, while the underside is called the thorax. The thorax bears five pairs of jointed legs, the first of which are provided with claws.

The shape and size of the claws of crabs differ greatly among the species, some being less than an inch in length while others are a foot or more. The claws are a most

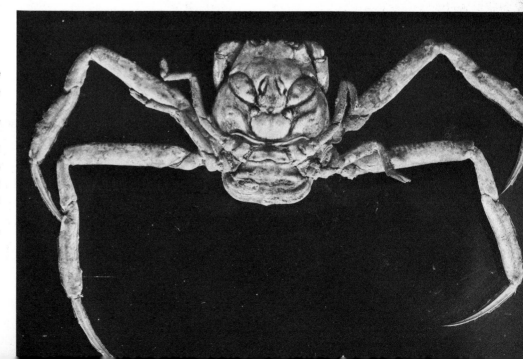

Left: Comparative size of the Alaska king crab (anomuran), male (left) and female.
Alaska Department of Fish and Game

The sculptured carapace of the Japanese mandarin crab resembles a fearsome face. It is often called the Japanese demon crab.
American Museum of Natural History

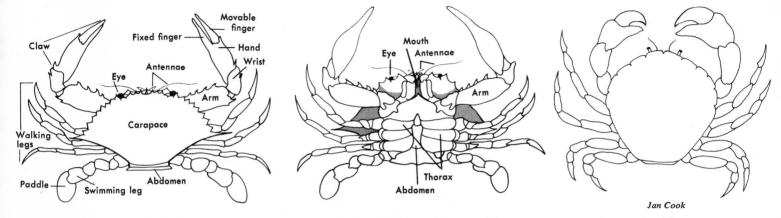

Left: Dorsal view of a blue crab. The rear legs are fashioned for paddling. *Center:* Ventral view of a blue crab. *Right:* Dorsal view of a mud crab. The rear legs are fashioned for walking.

important instrument, as they are used to obtain food and also as a defense against enemies.

The next three pairs of legs are used for walking, and the last pair are either of two types. Non-swimming crabs have hind legs ending in points, which help them to get a grip on rocks and to move easily over sand. In the swimming crabs, the last pair of legs usually have flattened paddles at the end to aid in propulsion through the water. Crabs can walk in any direction but, due to the formation of their jointed legs, they generally move along the ocean bottom and run across the sand in a sideways manner.

The compound eyes of the crab are situated at the end of movable stalks which extend out from under the front of the carapace. The eyes can be moved freely, making it possible for the crab to see in many directions and also allowing the eyes to be withdrawn in time of danger.

Located between the eyes are two pair of antennae. These sense organs receive physical and chemical stimuli. In other words, they are the means of touching and tasting for the crab.

Below the antennae and the eyes, on the underside of the crab, are six pairs of movable parts around the mouth. As a crab grasps food with its claws, it carries it to the mouth parts which serve as jaws for tearing and crushing the food before it enters the mouth.

Crabs are scavengers and form a type of clean-up squad as they feed upon dead and dying sea life. They eat sea urchins, sea cucumbers, bivalve mollusks, and fish, as well as algae and other plants. Crabs are also cannibals in that they are known to fight one another, and the loser is eaten by the victor.

The internal organs of a crab, which include the digestive, circulatory, and respiratory systems, are located more or less in the center of the body. The muscular parts, located on both sides of the organs, are divided into sections and separated by thin, shelly partitions. The many partitions or muscular chambers make it difficult to extract the tasty white morsels of the edible crabs that people consume.

Where the crab spends the majority of its life affects the size and number of gills which supply the oxygen necessary for life. A crab's gills are located in two chambers within the shell where they are protected from damage. In water-dwelling crabs, the

feathery, spongy gills take up most of the gill chamber. When the animal is submerged, water can be made to flow through the gills easily, thus supplying the needed oxygen.

Land crabs, as compared with their water-living cousins, have reduced the number and size of their gills. This allows the gill chamber to serve as a lung chamber to an efficient extent, yet sufficient gill tissue is retained for the animal to get along well enough under water.

Important to the crab's survival on land is the hard outer shell which keeps the animal from drying out quickly. It is not surprising then that some crabs are inclined to leave the sea and shoreline to explore what food and protection may lie above the high-tide line. When the time for reproduction comes around, though, the female land crabs have to go into water to hatch their eggs, as they have the same aquatic larvae as other crabs, which must pass through their earliest stages in water.

After mating, the females of all species start to lay their eggs, which they deposit between the abdomen and body in a special kind of glue-like substance. As more and more eggs are laid, the abdomen or tail is forced out and away from the body and acts as a cradle for holding the spongy mass of as many as two million eggs. The mother crab, called a "sponge crab" during this time, carries her eggs around with her in the water for about two weeks before they hatch as larvae.

The crab larva, or zoea, is transparent after leaving the egg and in no way resembles a grown crab. The zoea moves about through the water, eating and developing into the second larval, or megalops, stage, when it looks a bit more like a crab. Two

A land crab, Florida. Land crabs in great concentration can ruin a crop of young tomato plants.

American Museum of Natural History

months or more are spent in the larval stages before the change to adult appearance is complete, and in approximately a year a crab reaches maturity.

Crab larvae start out as very small creatures, about 1/25 of an inch in length, and help make up the microscopic sea life known as plankton. Millions of the larvae are eaten by hungry predators, but many survive. Small types of crabs live for two or three years, while large kinds may live to be fifteen or twenty years old.

The manner in which a crab increases in size is interesting and unique. The hard shell of the crab does not expand, so the growing crustacean must exchange its old shell for a new, larger one. The process of changing or shedding shells is called molting. The actual shedding process, which takes about an hour to accomplish, starts when the shell of the crab splits across the back end, just where the tail begins to turn under. The crab backs out of the old shell: its body, legs, mouth parts, and feelers are all drawn out. Even the outside lining of the stomach is shed with the shell. During the molting period, a crab does not eat. Most of the blood in the claws flows into the body, and lime in the joints of the claws dissolves. The muscles of the claws shrink because of loss of blood and are thus able to pass through the small, soft joints of the old shell.

The new shell that has formed inside the old one is soft and wrinkled. In this state the crab is called a "soft shell." Some kinds of crabs, especially blue crabs, are considered to be extra delicious eating when they are in the soft-shell stage.

Until a crab's new shell has become hard enough to protect its soft body, the creature does little but hide to protect itself from its enemies. After a two-day period, the

This mother blue crab is called a "sponge" crab because of the spongy mass of eggs she carries. As the eggs are laid, the tail is pushed away from the body, creating a pouch for carrying the eggs.

Texas Parks and Wildlife Department

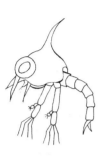

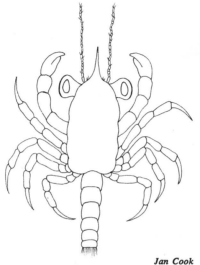

Jan Cook

Zoea, or crab larva (left), and megalops, or second larval stage, both greatly enlarged.

This series of cast shells was collected from one individual of an English shore crab. The crab molted seventeen times over a period of three years, and all its cast shells are shown except three which were accidentally destroyed.

British Museum of Natural History

wrinkled shell has stretched out and hardened, the crab begins to feed once more, and the process of filling up the shell begins all over again.

Baby crabs change their shells as many as seven or eight times in a year, while mature crabs usually molt only once a year.

If you find an empty crab shell and want to determine if it is a molt or the shell of a dead crab, you may lift off the top part of the shell. If it is a molt, you will find the cast off gills on each side of the stomach. You will also notice the lining of the stomach.

Blue crab showing regeneration "bud" which will grow into a new claw. This picture gives a good view of the thorax, or underside, of a crab.

Texas Parks and Wildlife Department

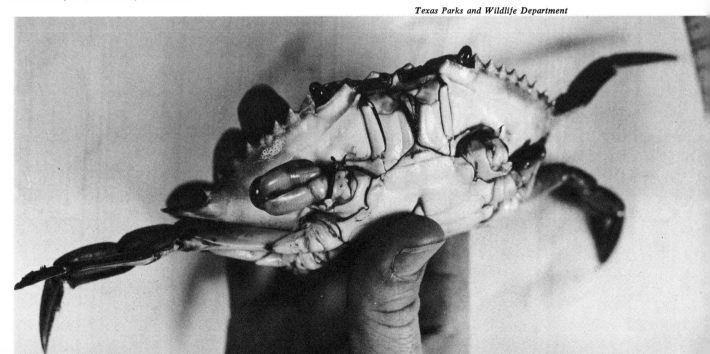

If the shell you find is the remains of a dead crab, there will be no slit across the back end, and inside you will see bits of flesh still clinging to the shell.

An interesting characteristic associated with growth in the crab is autotomy, the power to throw off appendages voluntarily. Near the bases of the claws and legs are definite breaking planes or points which allow a crab to drop off an injured claw, or if caught and held by a leg, to release that leg and escape.

Lost appendages are replaced with new ones by the process known as regeneration. After losing a leg the breaking point constricts so there is little bleeding, and in a few days a bud-like growth occurs, then a small limb, and finally, after months or even years, a full-sized leg replaces the old one.

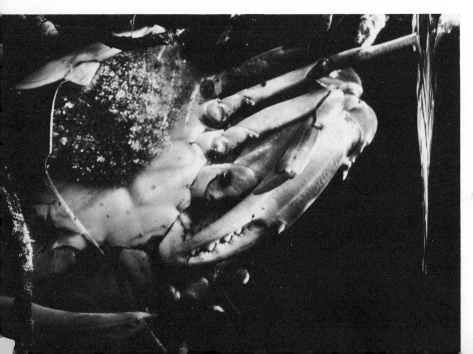

The ventral side of a female blue crab showing the egg masses.

American Museum of Natural History

3. Various Crabs of the World

BLUE CRAB

The blue crab lives in the shallow water of the bays and rivers of the Atlantic Coast from New England southward along the Gulf coasts to the northern shores of South America. It prefers brackish water—a mixture of salt and fresh water near the mouths of rivers and inlets—moving into deeper water in the winter to hibernate in the mud. During warm weather blue crabs are found clinging to docks and piers where they are easily netted by amateur fishermen.

This crab has an olive brown or dark green back shell or carapace, and a white or yellowish underside. Its oval shell is twice as wide as it is long, averaging six or seven inches. Each side of the carapace is drawn out into a long, sharp spine, with sixteen small spines along the front edge of the shell. Its legs and claws are tinted a bright blue and this is the reason for its name. The claws of the female are also tipped with red. Usually the right claw of a blue crab is heavier and bears blunter, broader serrations.

Blue crabs make use of all sorts of hiding places, striking out from them to capture unwary fish and other forms of marine life. It will eat almost anything, both plant and animal life.

These crabs are rapid swimmers, their back pair of legs ending in little paddles which are used as a boatman would use oars to row a boat.

The blue crab, popularly called the "blue claw," is extremely good eating and is caught by the thousands by fishermen. A dozen or so boiled, hard-shell blue crabs are a delicacy and a real feast. Some of these crabs are sold just after they have molted and before the new shells have hardened. These are called soft-shell crabs and are delicious fried or sautéd.

There are several ways to catch blue crabs, and the thought of their excellent taste adds to the thrill of crabbing. One method of capturing the creatures is with a crab trap. The trap has four sides, and at the top and middle of each of these four sides strong cord is tied. Then the four cords are tied to another stronger and longer piece of cord which will lower and lift the trap in and out of the water. Bait, such as dead fish, is tied in the bottom of the trap. As the trap hits the bottom, its four sides will fall open, allowing the crabs to reach the bait. When the fisherman pulls on the main cord, the sides of the trap will lift up, enclosing the quarry.

Another way to catch these delicious crabs is by using what is known as a killy ring. To make one of these, put a piece of wire through the bodies of some dead killies or other small fish and then hook the ends of the wire together so the bait cannot slide off. Tie a long piece of cord to the wire ring. Holding the cord in one hand, throw the

Catching blues
Texas Parks and Wildlife Department

baited ring into the water. Soon, if there are crabs present, you will feel a pulling on the line as the crab uses its claws to rip flesh from the killy ring. When you feel this, slowly pull in the cord until you have the clinging crab near the surface of the water and then scoop it up quickly with a crab net. A crab, or dip, net has a long handle and can go quite deep into the water.

A third way to catch blue crabs is to use only a crab net. These animals often stay near docks and piers, hanging onto the sides just below the top of the water. If you find one on a dock piling, quickly slip the net under him and you will have him. This is not easy, but it is fun. Sometimes blue crabs rest on the bottom of a shallow creek or hang on the banks of a canal. If you see one, perhaps he can be scooped up with the net. This takes agility and speed on the part of the fisherman because the blue crab is extremely fast moving.

When fishing for blue crabs it is wise to keep your catch separated, as the hard-shell crabs will eat or crush the soft-shell ones if they are thrown together.

The blue crab, with its two powerful claws, is an aggressive fighter and quickly attacks when cornered. "Blue claws" are fun to catch and a mess of them is truly good eating.

HERMIT CRAB

One of the most unique crabs is the hermit. Unlike other crabs, the hermit only has a heavy coat of armor on its front end. Its soft hind parts have no protection. It has never developed a shell or carapace there. To gain protection from birds, fish, or other crabs, the hermit borrows a discarded sea shell as a "house" which it carries around wherever it goes.

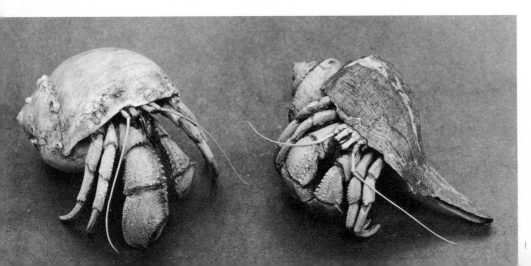

Hermit crabs live in discarded sea shells. As the crab grows, it seeks a larger shell for its house.

American Museum of Natural History

The hermit backs its soft, unprotected rear parts into the spiral of an empty shell with a twisting motion of its body. The crab keeps four legs inside the shell, using two as hooks to help hold the shell in place. The other four legs outside the shell help the crab to move about, while the sharp claws rip and tear the food that it eats. When the hermit retreats within the shell the opening is closed by the two claws which make a tight-fitting door. Smaller hermit crabs seek out shells of periwinkle and mud snails, while larger hermits use tulip, whelk, and moon shells to protect their soft, curved abdomens.

The hermit crab is often protected in another way, also. Sometimes barnacles or limpets grow on the hermit's shell-house, making it look like part of the sea bottom and helping to hide the crab from its enemies.

Hermit crabs are almost any color. Their feelers are sometimes red while their eyes are usually a bright, shiny black.

Early in the spring the female crab develops clusters of eggs which cling to her body inside the protective shell. When fertilized the eggs hatch and go through a swimming stage, then a stage in which they resemble tiny crayfish or lobsters. After this they molt and develop a curved abdomen. Then they have to find a small shell to cover themselves. When the crab grows and molts again, it is too big for the shell it is carrying and must move into a larger one. Changing from one shell to another is a dangerous time in a hermit crab's life and the crab is aware of it. It pulls the old shell close to the new shell and then makes a jump, out of one and into the other, back end first. This is probably the fastest house-moving on record.

A preserved hermit crab removed from a conch shell to show its soft, unprotected abdomen.

Jack Dermid — Photo Trends

By using empty sea shells as portable houses, the hermit has an out-of-water advantage in that the shell, on land, provides a moist chamber that keeps the crab from drying out. A few hermit crabs have learned to live out of water completely. Oxygen, of course, is still essential to life and the crab takes it from the air, through his gill chambers.

In the mangrove swamps in Florida, hermit crabs live in trees. The animals choose various types of shells, and when they swarm over the trunk of a tree they make it look as if it were a tree of shells.

The hermit crab is an odd fellow, using the shell of a dead animal as it does for protection. The hermit will use some other suitable shelter if there is no shell available. Some of these crabs that live in the East Indian waters have been seen with the abdomen stuck in half of a coconut shell or in a joint of bamboo.

Hermit crabs are mainly found in tide pools and shallow water all around the world. Here they eat the tiny sea plants and algae that grow on rocks. They also eat tiny sea animals, and each other if given the opportunity.

The curving, erratic trail of a hermit crab. The lengthwise groove was made by the dragging shell.
American Museum of Natural History

COCONUT OR ROBBER CRAB

The coconut crab, one of the best-known land crabs, is found on the islands of the South Seas. The crab bears two names due to the fact that it eats the nuts from the coconut palm, approximately one a day per crab, and thus robs the native communities of an important export item. This crab, growing to lengths of eighteen inches, lives in a burrow at the foot of a coconut palm where it is known to store coconuts for future use. The burrow is lined with the husks that the robber has stripped from the coconuts with its strong and heavy claws. The animal uses its claws to hammer at the nut until the shell cracks, making it possible to scrape out the meat.

The robber crab is related to the hermit crab but has given up the need of a portable dwelling and has become covered by shelly plates of armor. The robber is a nocturnal, or night, animal, and often spends the daylight hours sleeping in coconut trees which some scientists believe they do as protection against rats.

The coconut crab is a strong fighter and has few enemies except man and rats. The Chinese are very fond of this crab's flesh and in regions where the crabs are plentiful they keep them tied, as you would a dog in your backyard, and fatten them up for a delicious meal.

The islanders find this crab a tasty dish also. In his book *Crustaceans*, Waldo L. Schmitt cites two methods of catching the robber crab. When one of these crabs is sighted up a palm tree, a native will climb part way up himself, tie a girdle of grass around the trunk, and then climb down again. At nightfall the crab leaves its hiding place, crawling backward down the trunk of the palm tree, feeling behind as it de-

The coconut or robber crab of the South
Sea Islands is a land crab and grows
to lengths of eighteen inches.

British Museum of Natural History

scends. When it touches the grass encircling the tree, the crab, believing it has reached the ground, lets go of the tree trunk and falls to its death, or at least it is stunned enough to be picked up safely. In some instances, rocks are placed at the tree base to assure the crab's being killed in the fall.

Hunting the coconut crab is considered an exciting sport. This is carried on at night when the crabs become active; therefore the hunters must carry lanterns and torches. Faced with these enemies, the crab holds its claws in a protective position, guarding its face and soft abdomen, backing off several times but never turning away. Surprised momentarily by the lights, the crab is grabbed quickly by the back and held firmly at arm's length until it is otherwise secured. The captor must be extremely careful of the animal's claws as they can easily amputate a man's fingers.

This tree-climbing coconut robber lives its life on land, but like all crabs must go down to the sea when its eggs are ready to hatch so that the cycle of crab life can be repeated.

FIDDLER CRAB

The fiddler crab is a small burrowing animal found on sandy or muddy beaches, salt marshes, and even fresh-water streams in temperate and tropical zones.

The female fiddler has two small spoon-like claws but the male has only one of these. The other claw in the male is enormously enlarged and is moved back and forth in the fashion of a fiddler or violinist playing a violin. This large claw is used in mating-season battles and some scientists believe the male fiddlers communicate

The female fiddler crab has two small claws while the male has one small and one large. The large claw is moved back and forth in the manner of a fiddler playing a violin.

American Museum of Natural History

in this manner. Normally the male's right claw is the large one. However, if it is broken off, due to a fight or other causes, the remaining left claw will grow big and a new small claw will grow from the right side. Thus, the male fiddler becomes left-handed.

Hordes of these fiddler crabs can be found living together in communities where the ground is riddled with their burrows. The entrance to a typical burrow lies just below the high tide mark. The burrows slant downward a foot or more and usually end in a horizontal room. The crabs dig the holes by packing the wet sand between their legs and then pressing it into pellets or little sand balls which are carefully removed from the burrow. Generally a new burrow may be recognized by the mound of sand pellets piled in front of the opening. Sometimes hours are spent in making the end room, the depth of which is determined by how far the crab must go to reach sand that is very damp but not wet, because fiddlers can be drowned.

After a baby fiddler crab has passed through its larval stages it leaves the water and is never able to swim again. It becomes an air breather but must live in moist conditions in order to keep from drying out.

Before each high tide the crab scurries into its burrow and plugs the opening with sand pellets to hold in the air and hold out the water. If the animal is taken by surprise and finds water seeping in without previous warning, it rushes to the entrance to pull more pellets inside to make a more sturdy barricade. In the fall, the crabs in the cold regions plug up their doors solidly and hibernate.

The coloring of a fiddler crab is an interesting phenomenon of nature. At night the

34

Right: Cast of a crab burrow over 30 inches long showing horizontal room at bottom. *Above:* Male fiddler at mouth of burrow. The large sand pellets have been dug out of the burrow; the small ones are food pellets from which organic particles have been removed.

American Museum of Natural History

crab is several shades lighter than it is during the daytime. Many studies of the relation of light and dark to color changes in the crab have been carried on by scientists. During daylight the crab has a dark spotted shell. Scientists do not know as yet whether the change serves to camouflage the animal or protect it from the sun's ultraviolet rays or perhaps regulate its temperature.

There is no doubt, however, that the change in coloration from pale at night to dark by day is closely related not only to the daily cycle of the sun but also to the tides. The fiddler becomes darkest when the tide is low; the period in the day when the crab is most active. It is at this time that the crab leaves the burrow and saunters forth into air and sun in a dark coat in pursuit of food. The peak of pigmentation comes exactly fifty minutes later each day, reflecting the twenty-four-hour, fifty-minute tidal rhythm.

The fiddler crab feeds by scooping sand into its mouth, straining out and swallowing the organic material, and forming the remaining sand into pellets which it discards.

GHOST CRAB

A sandy stretch of shore that looks deserted really may be haunted by ghost crabs. Ahead, something may appear and disappear so quickly one can't be sure it was there at all. However, stand perfectly still and after a minute or so a pale, pop-eyed, sand-colored crab may climb out of a hole and go tiptoeing, bowlegged, across the beach. Start toward it and it may sink or fall motionless on the sand, its eyes standing out on

Having discovered an occupied burrow, Timber, the ghost-crab hunter, begins his excavation. The sand flies as he nears his prey. When Timber loses interest in his game, the uninjured but annoyed crab escapes.

long stems, swiveled around to look at what is approaching. If one goes still closer the crab probably will suddenly make a wild dash and disappear down a hole in the sand.

A dog named Timber, that lives in Florida, is an outstanding hunter of ghost crabs. Timber sits or lies patiently on the beach, scanning the sand for ghost crabs. Once he spots one he bounds after the creature, causing the crab to dive down into its burrow. Timber then sticks his snout in the hole and, if his nose tells him the crab is there, he will start to dig. The sand flies in all directions and the hole dug by Timber may reach a depth of two or three feet, but he skillfully catches the ghost crab without suffering a single pinch or bite from its claws. After Timber has played with the animal awhile his interest wanes and the uninjured but ruffled crab quickly scurries off.

The ghost crab, like the fiddler, is a burrowing crab, found along the Atlantic Coast from New Jersey to Florida. It prefers drier areas of sandy beaches and salt

37

marshes than the fiddler crab. Its body color blends perfectly with its environment, almost making it invisible and providing its name. Ghost crabs scamper rapidly across the sand, moving in quick sideways directions, starting and stopping suddenly.

Few animals better illustrate how, in the process of evolution, life has in many instances moved from the sea onto the land. Although it lives on land, the ghost crab is actually a creature of the water and once a day must obtain a supply of water in order to breathe. It accomplishes this by going to the edge of the surf or bay and letting the sea water roll over its shell, thereby filling the gill cavity. The ghost crab must be looked upon as a true water breather living on land, just as the whale is an air breather living in the sea. The ghost crab is like a skin diver carrying his air supply in a tank on his back, except the crab has a built-in tank which it fills with water from which oxygen is obtained.

Ghost crabs are tied to the sea in yet another way. The female must go into the water to hatch her eggs. When the young crabs are ready to live ashore they prepare their first burrows on the beach near the water's edge where the tides pass over them. As the crabs grow older they move away from the water, back beyond the high-tide mark. But still, at least once a day, they must go back into the sea to wet their gills.

The depth of the ghost crab's burrow is determined by how deep the crab has to go to find the right amount of moisture in the sand. At the beach in the early morning, ghost crabs can be seen popping in and out of their holes, apparently housecleaning. They bring sand up under their legs, then throw it out of the burrows like a man digging a ditch with a shovel.

Pale and pop-eyed ghost crabs live on sandy shores

Jack Dermid — Photo Trends

Most of the crabs disappear by afternoon, either resting or sleeping in their burrows. But at night the beach is alive with the creatures searching for insects, dead fish, or any bits of food they can find. At this time they are safe from birds, except possibly a night heron.

If a flashlight is shone on a ghost crab, it is blinded and sits perfectly still as long as the light is on, but hurries into the shadows or its burrow when the light goes off. Even in darkness the crab can find its own particular home somehow. Although hundreds of these crabs live in communities together, each lives in a burrow by itself and tells any intruder to keep out by rubbing two parts of a claw together to make a shrill whirring noise.

As the days grow short and a chill comes in the air, the ghost crabs are seen less often. Then one cold day they enter their burrows and plug up the door. In the moist, still room at the bottom of their tunnels they sleep out the winter, not needing even to replenish the water in their gill cavities. When the warm spring returns, they come up through the sand again to go down to the sea for their daily dip.

A ghost crab can grow or regenerate a new claw when it loses one. But if it loses the big claw, it must wait for a whole new big claw to grow. It cannot swap or switch from right-handed to left-handed the way a fiddler crab can.

DROMIID CRAB

The dromiid, an inhabitant of reefs, conceals its vivid colors by holding a shell or a live sponge over its carapace. In this manner it may travel unseen by enemy or prey.

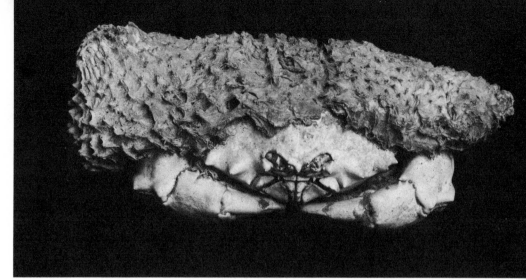

The dromiid crab camouflages itself by carrying a shell or sponge over its carapace. The sponge-carrying dromiid uses its claws, like scissors, to cut the sponge to the shape it wants.

American Museum of Natural History

The last pair of walking legs on this crab are reduced in size and turned up over its back so that the crab can hold its camouflage in place with them.

A shell-carrying dromiid's back is shaped so that it fits perfectly into the half of a clam shell. Often these dromiids are called clam-shell hermit crabs, for each time the crab molts and grows, it must find a larger shell to carry around just as a hermit crab does.

A sponge-carrying crab, on the other hand, can wear the same sponge a lifetime since the sponge is alive and increases in size right along with the crab, through all the moltings.

To obtain the correct shape of sponge-covering it needs for its back, this dromiid uses its claws like scissors, snipping and trimming the sponge to the size desired.

41

Dromiid crabs living in captivity, when deprived of the materials provided by nature for obtaining the protective cover of a shell or sponge, will use either pieces of paper or rags if these are placed in the tank with them.

The crab begins working at one edge of the material, tearing, moving along, and tearing again until the shape of its shell is cut out of the offered paper or cloth. Often times the crab methodically cuts the pattern of its shell while lying on its back beneath the material—the legs holding the sponge or artificial covering while the claws do the snipping and tearing.

Thus the dromiid crab, by an excellent display of artistry and craftsmanship, obtains a suit of camouflage, whether in its natural state or captivity.

STONE CRAB

The stone or rock crab, as it is sometimes called, is found along the southern Atlantic and Gulf coasts in shallow water where it hides under rocks and lives in deep burrows in the sand and mud. It is a beautiful-looking crab with a stout body about two-thirds as long as wide, with a hard, purplish or brownish-red shell. Its huge claws are black and banded with bright red and yellow. Some stone crabs reach weights of four pounds or more and measure two feet across between the outstretched claws. Whatever its size, the stone crab has amazing power in its claws and can do considerable damage to any animal that comes near it.

Many sea-food lovers consider the stone crab superior to all other crustaceans. The meat is firm, succulent, and tender, and has a distinct but delicate flavor. Only the

Texas Parks and Wildlife Department

The claws of the stone crab are considered a delicacy by sea-food lovers.

crab's claws are eaten, since the body contains a negligible amount of edible meat. In most areas where stone crabs are taken they are protected by laws so that only the claws or one claw may be removed. This is done by twisting or breaking off the claw at a joint. The crabber must be careful not to pull the claws out by the roots, as this will kill the crab. The body of the crab is returned to the water so that it can regenerate a new claw or claws and be taken again at a future date. Female crabs, if caught, must be returned to the water with claws left intact. The sex of the stone crab, as is true of all crabs, is determined by the shape of the abdominal flap on the underside. On the male this flap or tail is generally triangular; on the female, it is round.

Stone crabs are caught noncommercially in many ways. One of the most popular methods is to walk along the sand and mud flats at low tide, armed with a stick with a wire hook at the end. When the crabber sees a burrow he plunges the stick into the hole and hopes that the wire hook will help in pulling the crab from its hiding place. On a good day a crabber can come home with a nice catch of claws.

The stone crab was slow to gain recognition in this country as a food, and was actually considered inedible until the 1920's. Its value was discovered by a Harvard professor who came to Miami to study and classify the marine life of Biscayne Bay.

The professor had a mess of the crabs boiled and served in a restaurant in the same

The stone crab has amazing power in its claws. Here one is cracking oyster shells in order to feed on the oysters.
Texas Parks and Wildlife Department

way he usually prepared lobsters in New England. He found the claws delicious and persuaded the other customers to try them.

The new dish was an immediate success and led to a new sport for the amateur and a new industry for the fisherman.

GREEN CRAB

The green crab is found along the Atlantic Coast of North America from New Jersey to Nova Scotia, and on the Atlantic coastlines of England and Europe, where it is called a shore crab. It grows to be about two or three inches in width. As the name implies, it has an olive-green shell with a pattern of bright green on its back. The young crabs are green with black dots and markings on the back. Although the green crab is a swimming crab, its hind pair of legs, instead of being paddle-shaped, are flattened and end in points.

The average speed of a green crab traveling across the sand is about two feet in a second, but they are known for their ability to run at a rate of ten feet per second. These animals are extremely fast-moving whether in the water or on land.

The young of the green crab, being about thumbnail size, live in the marsh weed on land and come down to shallow bays and estuaries to hunt clams in these areas. The young crabs search the mud pockets, digging out pits and probing for clams that are about their own size. Adult green crabs live on shallow, rocky bottoms, between the tide lines, or in tidal pools except when they move into the shelter of weeds to molt.

The green crab is a vigorous swimmer even though he does not have paddle-shaped hind legs. He is a speedy traveler on the beach also.

American Museum of Natural History

This crab, once unknown north of Cape Cod, Massachusetts, has steadily progressed northward as far as Nova Scotia due to the rising water temperature over the years.

It has been suspected that in certain areas of New England the green crab has been killing off the soft-shelled clam, especially in the Gulf of Maine where the crab was unknown before 1930.

Though mostly caught as bait for fishermen, the green crab is edible and is often served in restaurants when broiled soft-shell crab is ordered, according to Dr. Donald Zinn of the University of Rhode Island. The annual catch of green crabs in each of the last several years has averaged sixty-five thousand pounds.

PEA CRAB

The pea crab is one of the many tiny crabs which belong to the group called commensals. Commensal crabs are found in all parts of the world wherever edible mollusks exist. Oysters, scallops, mussels, and various species of clams are infested with the pea-sized creatures. These whitish or pink crabs have an existence somewhat like a hermit crab in that they live in a borrowed shell.

Unlike the hermit crab, which lives in the empty shell of a dead animal, the commensals lodge inside live mollusk shells sharing the food of the host. The crabs are not parasites and only partake of the diet of tiny micro-organisms that the mollusks eat.

The males of commensal crabs are free swimming, but the females live their entire lives within their hosts' shells. As a result of its sheltered life, the female crab has a very soft and thin carapace or shell.

Scallops and mussels are the residences for pea crabs, while the oyster crabs live in the gill cavities of oysters.

A few commensal crabs have chosen other forms of life from which to obtain free board and room. A sponge of the Philippine Islands houses one type of these tiny crabs, while another type of pea crab is found on the Brazilian coast in a starfish.

The Dungeness or market crab (a rock crab) lives along the Pacific Coast from Alaska to California. It is caught commercially for sea-food markets.

California Department of Fish and Game,
Marine Resources Operations

ROCK CRAB

Rock crabs are found in all the seas of the world. Despite the name, these crabs are found living on sandy bottoms and in tidal pools, as well as on rocky bottoms and shores. The young crabs inhabit tide pools while the larger crabs prefer deep water in their search for food.

The legs of the rock crab are adapted to walking rather than swimming. The oval shell has blunt scallops along its front edge and each side. There are many species of rock crabs and they differ in their markings.

The rock crab prefers cooler water than most crabs and grows larger in the colder water. There are several related species, three to four inches in width, on the Atlantic Coast. The common rock crab of the Atlantic shores has a yellowish shell closely dotted with reddish-brown spots.

One crab of this group, found on the Pacific Coast from Alaska to California, is the edible Dungeness or market crab. This crab may attain a width of ten inches across the back and is caught commercially for sea-food markets where it is sold alive. Like the Atlantic species, it, too, has a reddish-brown shell. The Dungeness crab is highly valued for its flesh and is one of the main sources of crabmeat in the United States.

Emptying a catch of market crabs into a crate.

California Department of Fish and Game, Marine Resources Operations

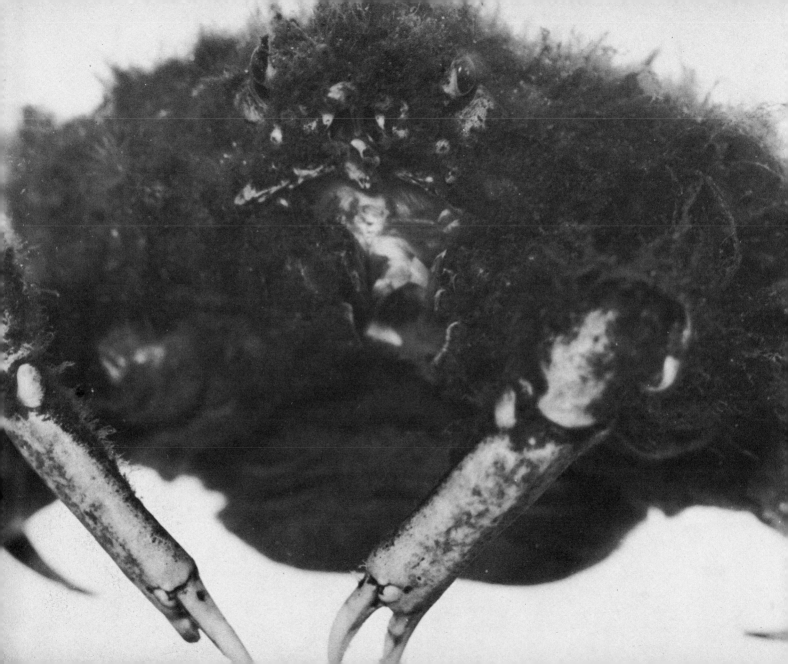

SPIDER CRAB

Spider crabs are found in the waters of both the Atlantic and Pacific oceans. They have a sac-like body, with the head at the narrow end and four pairs of unusually long, thin legs which make them resemble spiders. They also have a pair of long, leg-like slender claws.

There are many species of spider crabs, and although they are similar in appearance they differ in size, color, and temperament. The smallest specimen is one-half inch in length, while the giant spider crab of Japan, which is the largest known crab in the world, may span twelve feet between the tips of its outstretched claws.

Spider crabs do not burrow but live for the most part among seaweeds. Nature has

Left: A spider crab dressed in seaweed. The spider crab covers its back to match its surroundings, using seaweed, barnacles, algae, and other small organisms.

Marineland of Florida

A giant spider crab of Japan viewed by Waldo L. Schmitt, research associate for the Smithsonian Institution and author of the book, *Crustaceans.*

Courtesy of the Smithsonian Institution

THE GIANT CRAB OF JAPAN

provided these animals with hooked hairs on their backs to which the crabs can attach pieces of seaweed with their claws, thereby making it difficult for enemies and prey to see them. The crab chooses materials that match its environment and, when the creature travels to a new area, it will change the plant decoration to small animals if need be or even scatter pebbles over its back when in stony surroundings. Whenever the crab sheds its shell, the camouflage is discarded, too.

Numerous experiments have been conducted with these crabs in aquariums to prove that they can distinguish colors. Presented with strips of paper in a variety of colors, the crabs decorate themselves with pieces that match or more nearly match the color of their surroundings.

Many spider crabs are sluggish in nature and in spite of their long legs walk very slowly across the floor of the sea. All other crabs walk and run sideways but the spider crab is able to move obliquely or in a slanting manner as well.

Spider crabs have no commercial value and are considered a pest by fishermen. To get one off your fishing line while fishing can be an annoying job because the crab clings fiercely to the bait with its claws. So far, spider crabs are of no known value to man.

KELP CRAB

The kelp crab, which is found in the Pacific Ocean from British Columbia to lower California, is a relative of the spider crab but is otherwise unlike the average spider crab.

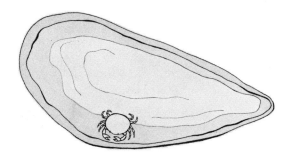

A tiny pea crab living in a mussel.

Jan Cook

The kelp crab likes to live in masses of seaweed.

Kelp crabs often inhabit rocky tide pools along Pacific beaches but more commonly live in kelp beds or masses of seaweed. It is difficult to detect these small, two-inch crabs among the strands of kelp since their olive-green shells match the seaweed.

The legs and bodies of these small animals have very sharp spines and their claws are extremely strong, which enables the crabs to cling to seaweed in the face of breaking waves and heavy storms at sea. Because of their powerful claws and spines, care must be taken in handling a kelp crab.

CALICO CRAB

The calico crab is pale yellow or brownish with patterns of dark-bordered blood-red spots on its carapace and legs. Many things marked with well-defined patches of

color, including fish, cats, and a fabric, have the name calico.

The calico crab is also known as the Dolly Varden crab. Dolly Varden, a character from Charles Dicken's novel *Barnaby Rudge*, became famous for her large straw hat trimmed with cherry-colored ribbons—a hat model that still comes into fashion now and then.

The colorful calico crab is found from Chesapeake Bay to Texas in deep or shallow water on all types of bottoms except clayey mud. The creature, sitting motionless with its legs and claws drawn close to its body, looks like pebbles or a rock to its enemies and prey. As small marine life moves by, the calico's large claws dart out and seize the food to pick apart and devour.

LADY CRAB

The lady crab is a swimming crab, its last pair of legs ending in broad paddles. Unlike most swimming crabs, this little specimen has a nearly circular shell that grows to be about three inches in size. The carapace is light colored and has an all-over speckled pattern of purple-red spots, so it is often called a calico crab. The true calico crab does not have swimming paddles, thereby making it relatively simple to distinguish between the two crabs.

The lady crab is common from Cape Cod to the Gulf of Mexico where it is found on sandy beaches from low-tide mark to shallow water. The animal usually lies buried in the sand with just its eyes sticking out, ready to thrust out its long claws and catch any passing food.

The colorful calico crab looks like the rocks and pebbles among which it sits.

Marineland of Florida

Lady crabs burrow in shallow water where they catch fish expertly with their toothed claws.

American Museum of Natural History

MOLE CRAB

Mole crabs received this name because of their mole-like shape and their ability to dig into the sand the way moles do in the earth. They are also known as sand crabs, sand bugs, or sand fleas.

The crabs, shaped somewhat like little lobsters with their tails tucked under, are not true crabs but belong to the anomuran group, along with king crabs and hermit crabs. Therefore, the last pair of legs are greatly diminished, being thread-like in the case of the mole crab with the remaining legs broad and flat for digging in the wet sand.

Mole crabs are animals of open beaches and as such are typically small, always fast moving. Theirs is a strange way of life, as each wave breaking on the beach is at once their friend and enemy; though the wave brings food, it threatens to carry them out to sea as it recedes. Only by amazingly rapid and constant digging can the animal survive the turbulent surf and shifting sand. These creatures continually go in and out with the tide so they do not have permanent burrows. All movements of the mole crab—swimming, digging, and crawling—are done backward. They burrow in the sand at the edge of the tide, digging in backward until only the tiny stalked eyes, the mouth parts, and the long, curling, feathery antennae on the head are exposed. Just

The inch-long mole crab lives in wet beach sand. All movements of the mole crab, swimming, digging, and crawling, are done backward.

American Museum of Natural History

as each wave begins to flow back to the sea, the mole crab sweeps the water with its plume-like antennae to catch minute food particles. When the water has receded, the crab pulls its feathers across its mouth, obtaining the food trapped there. As a wave washes toward shore the crab leaves the burrow, letting itself be carried along by the water until the wave slackens, then quickly backs into the sand again, collecting food from the receding wave. When winter comes the crabs leave the shore line and move into deeper water. Here they bury into the bottom and settle down to wait for the water to grow warm again in the spring.

The Atlantic Coast mole crab has a light yellowish shell while the Pacific Coast crab has a brown shell. In both species, the female carries her orange-colored eggs in an egg carrier under her abdomen for several months before they hatch and enter the water. As the time for hatching nears, the mother leaves the feeding movements of the other crabs up and down the beach and remains near the zone of the low tide, thus avoiding the danger of stranding her newly hatched offspring on the sands of the upper beach.

If you have the opportunity to visit the seashore you are almost certain to see a mole crab. Stand on the beach where an incoming wave will wash around your feet, and if you look carefully, you will probably notice a sudden shifting in the sand. Beneath the half-inch deep water you will see colonies of tiny objects popping out. They are visible for just a moment. As the wave recedes, the sand shifts again and the crabs are gone as suddenly as they appeared.

Many kinds of birds feed on the mole crab. If you watch a flock of sandpipers, or

American Museum of Natural History

Sandpipers and other birds feed on mole crabs.

small shore-line birds, you will see them wade along with the outgoing wave, picking furiously at the sand, then turn and rush shoreward as the next wave comes in. Larger birds, with their long legs, can stand quite still and let the incoming wave flow around them. Then, as soon as the mole crab pops out of the sand, the bird is ready to stab it with his beak.

Fish and other crabs, also, feed on the mole crab. Small fishes and crabs sometimes come right to the edge of the water to catch the little creatures. If a mole crab is caught by a wave and carried into slightly deeper water, a predator may quickly grab it. Fishermen often dig up mole crabs with a shovel and use them as bait. But when you turn over a shovelful of sand to search for mole crabs, you must be ready to move fast because when the crabs burrow into the sand, back end first, they go in a hurry. Also, they look like lumps of wet sand. Often before you can make up your mind which is sand and which is crab, the crab is gone.

PISTOL CRAB

The pistol crab is actually a shrimp but because of one enormously enlarged crab-like claw it is popularly called a crab. It is also known as a snapping shrimp and pistol shrimp.

The large claw of these little, inch-long creatures is equipped with a snapping device capable of making a pistol-like noise. The movable finger of the claw is provided with a plug or plunger which fits into a socket in the fixed finger of the claw. When the fingers of the claw close suddenly, like a man snapping his finger, the sharp report is heard.

Students of the sea have placed pistol crabs in aquariums to observe them. The noise from the pistol claw of just one of the tiny crustaceans can be heard all over a large room.

Like the fiddler crab, when both large and small claws are removed at their natural

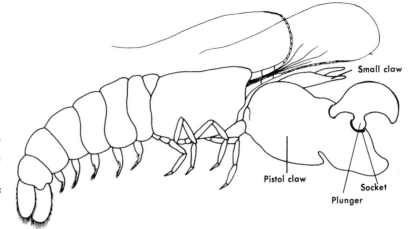

Small claw

Pistol claw

Socket

Plunger

The pistol crab or shrimp is an inch long. It is commonly called a crab because of its one large claw

Jan Cook

breaking joints, large and small claws grow again in their proper places. When only the large claw is removed, the small claw of the opposite side grows into a large claw.

The over-sized claw is so large in comparison to the body that the animal cannot withdraw the limb from the shell during the molting period. While the rest of the body sheds in the usual manner, the large claw shell breaks off in flakes.

The sound from the pistol claw is not just for the sake of making a noise but is actually a weapon. The "shot" repels an enemy or stuns small prey—defense and offense by concussion. Laboratory observation of these miniature animals have shown that they will hold a little fish or worm in the small claw while the prey is snapped and paralyzed by the large claw.

On the Pacific Coast, pistol crabs may be found under rocks and among sponges and seaweed. Along the Atlantic Coast they are found around oyster beds and in mud burrows. One species with a bright red snapping claw is commensal, living in the passages of sponges from North Carolina southward to the Gulf of Mexico.

A sponge, although it looks like a plant, is really a sea animal and has within itself a complicated system of canals, somewhat like the veins and arteries in a human body. To survive, the sponge must take in sea water through the holes in its body, pass it through the canals, and out again. From this constantly circulating supply of water the sponge strains tiny sea organisms called plankton on which it lives. Many thousands of varied, tiny animals living in the dark passages of a sponge also feed on the plankton. A scientist once removed nine thousand pistol crabs from inside a single sponge. It is interesting to note that a sponge has no known nervous system so the pistol-like shots made by the small, snapping crustacean have little or no effect on its host.

4. A Living Fossil

One of the oldest surviving species of animal living in the world is the horseshoe crab. This crab's shell is shaped like a horse's foot and that is how it received its name.

More than 200 million years ago there were living horseshoe crabs that were practically identical with those we see today. Their larvae are very primitive and are known as trilobite larvae since they closely resemble an extinct group, the *Trilobita*. Because of this resemblance it is believed that horseshoe crabs are descended from these fossil creatures. Horseshoe crabs first appear as fossils in ancient rock during the period known as the Cambrian. This is the earliest time from which scientists can really study living creatures. The animals have been preserved as fossils for us to see by sediment that covered and smothered some of them and then changed them to rock that has lasted through the millions of years down to the present.

The horseshoe crab is the last survivor of a group of animals that vanished from the earth millions upon millions of years ago. For this reason these creatures are sometimes called living fossils. They are one of the oldest representatives of the inverte-

Horseshoe crabs at the shore line

brates, or animals without backbones.

It wasn't until the sixteenth century that scientists discovered the horseshoe crab. The reason for this is that these creatures did not inhabit the seas near the lands where early scientists lived. In 1585, the first English colonists to settle in America observed the Indians' use of the horseshoe crab as food and as a means of catching fish. The hollow, stiff tail spine of the crab was attached to a long reed or stick with which the Indians speared fish. During the 1600's, as more and more of the Atlantic shore was colonized, fishermen up and down the coast became annoyed at the amount of these animals they hauled in with their nets and also the damage done to the nets by the crabs' tails and corners of the shells. However, it was discovered that the pigs and chickens of the settlements would clean the meat from the shells so it became worthwhile to catch the crabs for feed. Eventually it was found that, ground up, dried horseshoe crabs made good fertilizer for crops, and millions of the crabs were harvested and used this way right up until the 1950's when the catch had become so low that the fishery came to an end.

It wasn't until the twentieth century that famed British geologist Edwin Ray Lankester discovered that horseshoe crabs are not crabs and are related more closely to modern land scorpions and spiders than to any other creature alive, even though the relationship is distant. Because of its crab-like appearance and the fact that it sheds its shell periodically as all crabs do, the creature has always been called a crab.

The American horseshoe crab, scientifically known as *Limulus polyphemus*, lives along the Atlantic Coast of North America from Nova Scotia to the West Indies and along the Gulf of Mexico to Yucatan. None live on the coasts of Africa, Europe, Australia, or the Pacific Coast of the Americas. Several other species live along the shores of southeastern Asia and the East Indies, where they are caught and used for food.

The horseshoe crab's body is made up of three distinct parts which are hinged together. The large hood-like thorax or head is joined to the smaller, triangular-shaped abdomen by a hinge that works up and down. The long, tapered spine or tail is attached to the hind part of the abdomen in ball and socket fashion, allowing the tail

Three cast shells of horseshoe crabs washed onto the beach by the tide. When the horseshoe crab molts, it crawls out the front end of its shell rather than the rear of the shell as in the case of all true crabs. The horseshoe crab uses the sharp spine of its tail to turn itself over.

to swivel in any direction. Though bathers are many times frightened by the appearance of a horseshoe crab, these creatures are harmless to man. The tail is not a weapon but serves as a handy tool to the crab whenever the waves or other conditions have turned it on its back. When the animal finds itself in this predicament it thrusts the tip of its tail spine into the sand or mud at almost a right angle from the body and arches itself over sideways and right side up again. The body of a horseshoe crab, including the spine, can be approximately two feet long and from four inches to more than a foot across.

This unusual animal has four eyes to help it to navigate on both land and in the water. On the upper surface of the head, toward the front and center of the carapace, is a sharp spine which contains two small, simple eyes which enable the crab to tell night from day. Two other spines, farther back on each side of the head, shield the larger compound eyes. These eyes are as hard as the rest of the shell and are immovable. The dark area, known as the pupil of the eye, changes position whenever the crab turns.

The horseshoe crab has a unique sense of direction. It has been scientifically proven that these crabs can detect certain patterns in the light from the sky, whether on land or beneath the surface of the water. The light patterns that the crabs react to are brought about by the scattering of the sun's rays as they strike particles of dust in the air. The crabs know that by keeping the patterns of light in one position they will reach water, while the opposite direction leads to shore. On overcast days or moonless nights, horseshoe crabs limit their activity and just settle down on the bottom of the water to wait for clear skies.

The underside of the head houses six pairs of reddish-brown appendages. The first pair are short claws or pincers and the other five are legs. The first four pairs of legs end in very slender little claws which are used to grasp food and the last pair are tipped with spikes.

It is stated that the horseshoe crab walks, but even with ten legs it does not walk as one would imagine. The first four pairs of legs do not move the body forward at all. Instead, they lift the heavy body off the ground. The fifth or last pair of legs are the longest and the sharp spikes at the end are surrounded by several flanges or flaps. The flaps open at right angles to keep the legs from sinking into the sand as the crab pushes itself forward. When the first eight legs have lifted the body, the crab sticks his two back legs, like ski poles, into the ground and shoves. The crab lurches an inch or two forward before falling back into the sand or mud. Then the whole process has to be

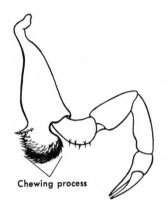

Chewing process

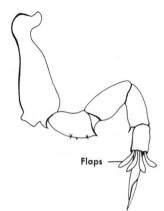

Flaps

Left: A lifting leg of the horseshoe crab, showing the spiny chewing process on its base.

Right: One of the rear or pushing legs of the horseshoe crab. Note the flaps which open at right angles and keep the leg from sinking into the sand as the crab pushes itself along.

Jan Cook

done again—the first eight legs lift the body, the back two push. Thus, the crab plows along like some strange mechanical toy.

A deep, narrow groove running between the legs forms the mouth of the crab. The bases of the first eight legs are equipped with short, rough bristles which serve as teeth. As the crab moves along, the bases rub together and grind any food that lies between, which then passes up into the mouth. This animal can never sit down to a meal, for the creature cannot eat unless it is moving, the two actions going together.

Food is obtained by slowly shoveling along the bottom of the sea with the flange of the large hood stirring up the sand and mud. Small creatures such as worms and soft shell clams which are plowed up are seized by the pair of small claws in front of the legs and passed back to the leg grinders. Usually the crab spits out the bits of shell, pebbles, and coarse sand before the food goes on into the intestine to be digested. However, like a bird, horseshoe crabs need some sand, pebbles, and bits of broken clams to help their muscular gizzards digest the food.

Behind the legs is the abdomen. The two rims of the abdomen shell that come together at the tail joint are edged with sharp prongs. In the notches between the prongs are short, movable spines, giving the crab a well-armored appearance. On the underside of this shell are six pairs of thin, broad flaps that overlap like shingles on the roof of a house. The first pair, housing the sex organs, are tough and leathery and are a protective covering for the others. The remaining five pairs are the breathing or respiratory organs. Known as gill books, they are so called because when in use the flaps wave like the pages of a book. Each of the ten books has about eighty pages or leaf-like gills through which blood flows. The books spread open in the water, and with a rhythmic beating motion of the pages or gills the animal draws oxygen from the water.

The horseshoe crab leaves a distinctive mark as it travels across the mud or sand flats. There will be two grooves, an inch to a foot apart, depending on the crab's size. Between the grooves, which are made by the hood shell, will be a combination of many footprints and a central line made by the dragging tail spine.

Horseshoe crabs can swim but they spend most of their time scooping in the mud or sand for something to eat. The animals usually go swimming at night. Perhaps this is the only time they are safe from hungry sea birds. To change from crawling to

Female (left) and male horseshoe crabs at Cape May, New Jersey.

Leonard Lee Rue III

swimming, the crab begins a slow run on the bottom. Rising as high as possible on its jointed legs, it propels itself forward, the legs and gill books beating rhythmically. All at once, the body tilts upward at the front and the crab does a backward somersault. The steady beating of the legs and gill books raises the inverted crab to the surface of the water where it continues to swim upside down, looking like a round-bottomed boat cutting through the water. When it rests, it slowly sinks. However, if the crab resumes the beat of its appendages, it rises again to the surface for another swim.

In early summer the female horseshoe crab crawls upon the beach between the high and low tide marks to lay her eggs in depressions where the high tide will wash sand over them. She makes the depression or nest by burrowing into the sand with her big armored shell. In each nest she lays as many as two or three hundred eggs, of tan or white color and the size of a pinhead. The male crab, which is smaller than the female, is hitched to the mother crab during this period and releases a fluid onto the eggs which fertilizes them. Finished at the first nest, the female and her mate crawl to another spot. Again she begins to dig. She makes a number of nests as she has about a quart of eggs to lay. Small fishes eat many of the eggs as soon as they are laid. Also, many are consumed if sea birds chance to discover the nests.

After a few days in the wet sand warmed by the sun, the hard outer covering of each egg bursts off. Underneath is another shell which swells up until the egg is twice as big as it was before. The new egg shell is almost as clear as glass and a tailless baby horseshoe crab is plainly visible inside. As each baby crab develops within the shell, it sheds its skin two different times before hatching. Some hatch in two weeks while others take as long as four weeks. The newly hatched crabs begin to swim on their backs as soon as they are free. While many are eaten by predators at this time, others are swept into the shallow waters of bays by the tides and quickly burrow into the sand for safety.

In a few weeks each of the crabs has shed its skin once more. At this time the animals are about a quarter of an inch long and have a tail spine for the first time. By late summer these baby crabs are approximately an inch wide and nearly twice as long.

As horseshoe crabs grow they shed or molt their shells. The hood splits open along the front and sides and the creature squeezes forward out of its shell, in contrast to crabs which pull out backward.

By the time a horseshoe crab is three years old it has shed its hard outer shell a total of eleven times and has grown to approximately three inches in width and six inches long. At this age the crab leaves the shallow water of the shore line and starts to migrate into deeper parts of the ocean where it will live on the muddy bottom for several years, feeding and growing. Between the ages of nine and eleven the crab reaches adulthood and travels back to shallow water where it will live out the remainder of its life.

One recent summer a horseshoe crab was inadvertently hooked in a swiftly moving channel and reeled into shore. It was a mature animal and the fisherman decided he would take the crab home with him to study and observe. For the time being the crab was placed in a pail with a wet cloth over it for protection against the heat.

The well-armored horseshoe crab is the last survivor of a group of animals that vanished from the earth millions of years ago. For this reason these creatures are sometimes called living fossils.

American Museum of Natural History

After the crab was brought home the question of where best to keep him arose. It was finally decided that the bathtub would make the most sensible home for the crab. The children of the family named the horseshoe crab Limulus, after its scientific name. At first Limulus wandered about the bathtub, probably seeking water and food. The family went to a bait store and purchased some marine worms and a few clams. These were placed in the tub and were eagerly eaten by Limulus, who proved that to eat he must walk. Every day when a member of the family took a shower, Limulus also received a shower. There was only one problem with having Limulus as a pet and that was the noise he made when he walked. His shell would bang down hard in the bathtub as he moved about. It was an eerie sound to hear in the middle of the night. The noise was so loud that the family couldn't sleep while Limulus took his nocturnal walk. So it was decided that the best place for Limulus was back in the bay. Before he was returned to the water, however, all members of the family saw how Limulus crawled on the front lawn and also how he used his tail spine to turn himself over. He was then placed in the car and taken to the bay. At first when he was put in the water he didn't move. But soon he began to crawl toward deeper water and in a matter of minutes he disappeared. So ended the bathtub saga of Limulus, the horseshoe crab.

Recently, scientists have discovered that no bacteria will grow in the blood of a horseshoe crab. The animal seems to contain its own antibiotic medicine. Also, nervous connections in the heart and the compound eyes are far more simple than those in human beings. The way the crab's nerves control these organs is so similar to the same process in man that scientists and medical people hope to find ways of aiding humans by studying this crab.

Man has done many things to cut down the population of the horseshoe crab. The animal was harvested for fertilizer indiscriminately. The building-up of shore front property has affected the mating and egg-laying processes. Garbage dumps built near waterways bring gulls, which in turn eat the young crabs. If the horseshoe crabs, considered "living fossils" because of their ancient lineage, are to survive, it is up to the foresight and intelligence of man to provide places where these animals can mate and lay eggs and so continue the species.

5. The Crab through the Ages

The very name "crab" is a synonym for a grouchy or disagreeable person. How many times have you heard or used the phrases, "Don't be a crab," or "Don't be crabby"? It is a common expression in the English language for unpleasant personalities and it is a reputation well deserved, since many crabs are pugnacious, mean little fighters. The common green crab of the Atlantic has so low a boiling point that, in France, fishermen call it *le crabe enragé* or "the angry crab."

Another behavioral characteristic of crabs that has added a common phrase to the language is their habit of walking and running sideways, a form of locomotion that sometimes develops surprising speeds. How many times in your gym classes or physical activities have you crab-walked?

We also use the word to describe a weed that gets into lawns. We call it crabgrass, and it probably received its name because it looks somewhat like a crab with a round center and many leg-like shoots striking out from the center of the plant. Crabgrass is the enemy of most gardeners and is considered quite a pest.

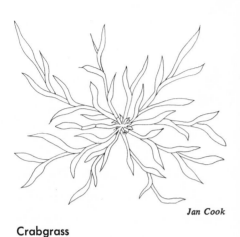

Crabgrass

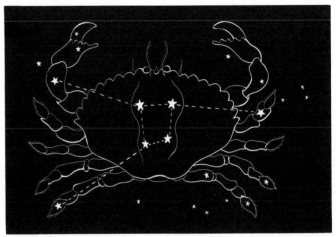

The constellation of Cancer the Crab.

The crab played a significant part in the myths and legends of ancient people. The Latin name for crab is cancer. The constellation of the crab is one of the faintest in the sky and yet it is a famous sign. When the extent of the signs of the zodiac were fixed and put in the order we now know, the stars of Cancer coincided with the northernmost point reached by the sun at midsummer. This is known as the summer solstice, or the sign of summer. As to why it should have been a crab, some said that it was because the peculiar, sidelong gait of the animal was just like the behavior of the sun when it reached the solstice. Arriving there, it seemed to hesitate, begin an oblique movement, and slide down across the sky like a crab inching sideways across a sandy beach.

The ancient Greeks believed that the goddess Juno, in one of her frequent fits of jealousy, sent a crab to attack Hercules at the very moment that he was engaged in his great struggle with the monster Hydra. The crab, according to the myth, bit Hercules on the foot and was quickly crushed to death in return. Juno placed the crab, so the story goes, in the sky as a reward for its services.

On every map of the northern hemisphere is noted the "Tropic of Cancer." Tropic is Greek, and means the turn or change which marks the most northern limit on the earth's surface at which the sun may be directly overhead and at which the sun seems to pause before retracing its course to the south.

During the decline of the Roman Empire, people were strong believers in the supernatural and the prophecies of astrologers. Zodiacal symbols invoking the influence of the stars were considered so powerful that rich and poor alike wore some form of jewelry engraved with their own particular sign of the zodiac.

Many beautiful gem stones and coins bearing the crab have been excavated in the valley of the Euphrates. Also, still in existence are fragments of temple paintings and palace wall reliefs of the ancient Mediterranean peoples dating from B.C. 1580 which bear representations of crabs.

The crab has also played an interesting role in literature. Rudyard Kipling in his *Just So Stories* tells of the crab that played with the sea, much to the distress of the land animals and the mighty Magician of the Universe. As a reward for stopping his

Representation of an ancient Roman ring engraved with the zodiacal symbol Cancer.

Jan Cook

rude behavior, the crab was given claws, the ability to live on land or in the water, and his hard shell, but as punishment he was forced to shed his shell and be soft for a time to remind him of what the Magician could do.

In Lewis Carroll's classic, *Alice's Adventures in Wonderland*, among the many strange, talking animals that Alice encounters is a mother crab who advises her daughter to hold her snappish temper.

The crab is found in an ancient Roman fable and also in poetry. One poem which describes a crab quite accurately in just four lines is a Chinese verse from a collection known as *Chinese Mother Goose Rhymes*.

OLD CHANG THE CRAB

Old man Chang, I've oft heard it said,
You wear a basket upon your head;
You've two pairs of scissors to cut your meat,
And two pairs of chopsticks with which to eat.

A nonsense poem written by Edward Lear also uses the crab as a major character:

> There was an old person of Hyde,
>
> Who walked by the shore with his bride,
>
> Till a Crab who came near fill'd their bosoms with fear,
>
> And they said, "Would we'd never left Hyde!"

Lear also included the crab in his "Nonsense Botany," a collection of drawings with nonsensical Latin names.

Crabs have appeared in literature describing some of man's most heroic adventures. In his famous book, Thor Heyerdahl tells of some interesting incidents with crabs

Below: The crab Edward Lear used to illustrate his limerick resembles a beetle. *Right:* The author-artist did rather better with the crab in his *Nonsense Botany.*

Crabbia Horrida.

during his Pacific Ocean voyage on the small raft *Kon-Tiki*. One of these incidents describes the *Kon-Tiki's* drifting along and being boarded by guests, to the surprise of the crew. These were small open-sea crabs which crawled up from the ocean. The first ones the crew saw were floating on a bird's feather. Two or three small crabs sat on it, sailing along with the wind. Soon these and others were all over the raft, filling themselves with everything edible on board. At one point eight or ten of them were seen helping themselves to a flying fish. The crabs ate anything, and if a scrap of bread or bit of fish was thrown before them they came right out of their hiding places, picked at it with their claws, and then devoured it.

In agriculture, the crab is both a villain and a benefactor. While some crabs burrow and thereby drain rice paddies with a resultant loss of crops, others help to build soil on coral reefs by collecting seaweed, seeds, twigs, and bits of coconut into their burrows. Thus rich vegetable mold accumulates on the atolls.

Crabs have been featured in the field of medicine, Pliny telling us that the ancients considered the crab, or the ashes of a crab, swallowed with water to be an antidote for poison. The Chinese too believed that fossilized crabs neutralize poison. And recent research has found that crustaceans are health-giving food, containing iodine in an organic combination and glycogen.

Down through the ages and into the present, the crab has played an interesting and important, and oftentimes amusing, part in the lives of men.

6. Harvesting the Sea

Up in Alaskan waters there lives the huge, exotic crab commonly called the king crab. Scientifically, these are known as *Baralithodes camtschatica*, a giant crustacean that inhabits the waters of the North Pacific. This amazing sea animal was envisioned as a food potential for American markets by a Captain Lowell Wakefield in 1941. Captain Wakefield witnessed a seldom-seen phenomenon which occurred at low tide off the island of Kodiak. He saw what looked like "haystacks" in the sea. Only a few fishermen sailing off the bleak coast around Alaska have seen this sight. There were hundreds of the giant king crabs, piled one on top of another in a huge pyramid, something scientists cannot explain.

Quickly, some of the crabs were harvested, and after cooking the animals the crew had a wonderful meal from the delicate and tasty meat of the claws and legs. The legs and claws of a king crab may have as much as four pounds of meat, but the body contains little that can be eaten and so is discarded.

Some of these vicious-clawed monsters are six feet in length from tip to tip, and

some specimens exceed twenty pounds in weight. The average weights run from seven to nine pounds.

After World War II ended, Captain Wakefield decided to try crabbing as a new American industry in Alaska, even though the Japanese had been netting king crabs in the North Pacific commercially for years.

The Alaskan captain had an idea. He decided that, rather than take the crabs alive to the market, he would cook or boil them on the ship and then freeze the delicious meat quickly. Then they would be ready for the market fresh from the sea.

Captain Wakefield had a specially designed 140-foot trawler, the *Deep Sea*, built. It contained the latest type processing and freezing plant and it also had the hull of an ice breaker. Its zero-degree refrigerator storage space was as large as that of eleven refrigerator railroad cars. The vessel quartered twenty-two men and had the use of wartime-perfected radar and sonar for making the operation successful and profitable. The *Deep Sea* was the costliest fishing ship ever to fly the American flag.

The *Deep Sea* trawled the seas with nets of handmade Irish hemp 150-feet long and 120-feet wide. As the ship plowed through the ocean, its net planed out. The face of the net was kept open by one-ton flat doors attached on either side. The crew towed at one hundred fathoms, or six hundred feet, with fantastic results; from three hundred to eight hundred crabs an hour were harvested.

Once aboard, the crabs were dumped into tanks of circulating sea water. Removed from the depths of the sea, the creatures became sluggish and easily manageable. They were washed, put into wire baskets, and immediately plunged into boiling

Alaska king crabs. The lower specimen is a rare Albino.
Alaska Department of Fish and Game

Unloading a good catch of king crab, Kodiak Island. The *Deep Sea* is in the background.

sea water and cooked. The meat was then removed from the legs and claws, frozen in blocks, and covered with a freezing glaze of fresh water, ready for packaging. The *Deep Sea* could hold 170 tons of crab meat. When the ship was loaded to capacity she headed back to port with her product.

It took three years for a profitable market to be built. The demand soon outstripped the supply and other methods were employed to catch this delicacy of the North. Today, king crabs are often taken by "pots" or steel traps baited with herring or various bottom fish. Each pot has a buoy and line to lift it from the bottom. Common sizes of the pots are six feet by six feet, seven feet by seven feet, and eight feet by eight feet. The pots may weigh as much as eight hundred pounds so that they can stay put during storms and in strong tides. King crabs are taken in all parts of Alaska, but present catches are mostly from Cook Inlet, Kodiak, the Aleutian Islands, and the eastern Bering Sea.

The highest catch, so far, occurred in 1965 and was 157,000,000 pounds. The catches average in the neighborhood of 110,000,000 pounds per year. From the thoughts and dreams of one man, a great industry that serves man everywhere has become a reality.

The blue crab is the most valuable commercial crab found along the Atlantic and Gulf coasts of the United States. Economically, it is the crab of the fishing industry and brings, at the present time, more than five million dollars to the crab fishermen. One of the major areas where the blue crab industry centers is Chesapeake Bay, with its many

Unloading king crab from bottom-trip bucket into processor's live tank.

King crabs coming out of vessel hold in "monkey cart." Crab pots are to the right of the hold hatch.

Alaska Department of Fish and Game

"Monkey cart" ready to hoist crabs into cannery live tanks.

King crabs in cannery live tanks. All crabs are kept alive until processed.

Alaska Department of Fish and Game

Fisherman removing king crab from pot.

Alaska Department of Fish and Game

smaller inlets and brackish rivers which empty into the bay. During its lifetime the blue crab migrates the length and breadth of the Chesapeake Bay. Spawning takes place near the mouth of the bay, and the larval or early stages of life are spent there. When the crabs have passed through the early juvenile stages and matured, most of them begin the trek which will eventually take them to all regions of the bay and its tributaries, where more than 150 million are caught annually. Louisiana waters also abound with crab life and there are several crab-processing plants in Texas which are helping to meet the ever-increasing demand for crab meat. An average of 125,000 pounds of crab meat per month is estimated for a typical coastal plant.

Crabs are primarily used in the form of picked crab meat. The meat is picked from hard-shell crabs that have been steamed and is shipped to market in iced containers, or it is canned. The much relished soft-shell crabs are shipped to market alive.

Hard crabs are caught by trotline and by baited traps known as "pots." The trotline is a long length of rope, weighted at each end, with pieces of bait such as eel, tripe, or bacon rind tied to it about three feet apart. It is laid on the bottom of the bay

The blue crab pot is baited and lowered into the water. The crabs enter the pot through funnels to get the bait and are then unable to find their way out.

Texas Parks and Wildlife Department

89

Market crab trap. Crabs under the legal size are able to leave the circular steel traps through an escape hole.

California Department of Fish and Game, Marine Resources Operations

with its ends marked by small buoys. To collect the crabs, the fisherman runs his boat along the line, forcing the line to pass over a roller attached to the boat. As the boat progresses, the crabs cling to the bait until they reach the surface, where the crabber catches them in a dipnet and places them in a basket or barrel.

The more popular method of catching crabs today is the pot or trap. The baited pot is set in selected points in the water ranging in depth from fifteen to thirty feet. The pot is cube shape, two feet on a side, and made of one inch poultry wire. The crabs enter the pot through funnels to get the bait and are then unable to find their way out. During the winter months the blue crabs hibernate in muddy sand and weedy bottoms, and at this time metal dredges are used to dip up the reluctant crustaceans.

The individual soft crab is more valuable commercially than the hard crab; however, fewer are caught. They are obtained mostly by holding peeler crabs in floats until they are ready for market. Peeler crabs are crabs that are just beginning to peel or shed their hard shell. Peeler and soft crabs are caught by pulling a large, toothless dredge called a "scrape" over the bottom by means of a boat. The places generally chosen for this operation are good shell-shedding areas typified by a cover of eel grass. Soft crabs are also caught by poling a small boat along shallow areas and dipping the crabs with a long-handled net. This method is less expensive but is not broadly used on a commercial basis.

The Dungeness or market crab is exploited commercially from Alaska to California. The total poundage landed for the Pacific Coast is around thirty-five to forty million pounds per year. California alone averages about 1.7 million dollars per year on its Dungeness crab market.

A typical catch of market crabs ready to be unloaded at the dock and taken to market.

California Department of Fish and Game,
Marine Resources Operations

California Department of Fish and Game,
Marine Resources Operations

Left: The old method of pulling traps by hand is still in use on many vessels. *Right:* An hydraulic power block is now in use on the more efficient boats for pulling traps from the water.

There are slight differences in seasons and regulations between the West Coast states. However, the fishery is controlled and supervised by all to protect the crabs during the summer molt. This allows the crabs to be in prime condition for harvesting. The catch is limited to males and only crabs six-and-a-quarter inches or more are taken. Those crabs less than the legal size are able to leave the circular steel traps through an escape hole designed to keep in the larger crabs. Traps are generally fished overnight but poor fishing or weather often increases this to several days.

Because the meat of these crabs is difficult to keep, the bulk of the catch is sold alive or freshly cooked to customers.

Some of the San Francisco crab fleet.

*California Department of Fish and Game,
Marine Resources Operations*

The stone crab industry is limited mainly to Florida. The meat from stone crab claws, which is the only part of the crab used, is a delicacy, and when boiled and dipped in lemon butter it is considered by many to rank among the finest sea foods. Like other sea animals, it is an excellent source of protein, minerals, and vitamins.

Stone crabs are caught commercially with traps constructed of wooden laths with one to one-and-a-half inch spaces between the slats. The over-all dimensions are eighteen by one foot by one foot. The baited traps are weighted with a concrete slab in the bottom and buoyed so the fisherman will know where his traps are located. The traps are usually pulled up and re-baited every other day. The stone crab is caught in depths ranging from twelve to thirty feet.

Crabs are a good source of food to marine life as well as to man. There is great potential in the crab and it is to be hoped that more and more research will be directed toward this unique animal, some species of which live deep in the water while others dwell in trees. The crab as one member of the crustacean family is indeed a curious creature as it roams the shores and seas of the world.

This cub scout from Alaska is being given a few pointers on king crab biology, and the value of SCUBA as a research tool in biological investigation.

Alaska Department of Fish and Game

INDEX

ABOUT THE AUTHOR

JOSEPH J. COOK received his B.A. degree at Drake University and his M.S. from the State University College, New Paltz, New York, following three years in the Army during World War II. He also attended Columbia University and served as a reading analyst for a major publishing house. Mr. Cook has been an educator on Long Island for many years, is an editorial consultant for a children's magazine, and lectures at Hofstra University. He is a confirmed student of wildlife, as well as a strong advocate of conservation.